BLUFF YOUR WAY IN WEATHER FORECASTING

DAVID MILSTED

RAVETTE BOOKS

Published by Ravette Books Limited
3 Glenside Estate, Star Road
Partridge Green, Horsham,
West Sussex RH13 8RA
(0403) 710392

Series Editor – Anne Tauté

Cover design – Jim Wire
Typesetting – System Graphics Ltd.
Printing & Binding – Cox & Wyman Ltd.
Production – Oval Projects Ltd.

The Bluffer's Guides are based on
an original idea by Peter Wolfe.

CONTENTS

THE WEATHER

There's a lot of it about. All around us. And it's popular. In tests, 8 out of 10 conversationalists (as opposed to Conservationists, who can only talk *at* people) said they preferred it to sex, Kylie Minogue and whether Penguin should publish a scratch'n'sniff edition of *The Satanic Verses*.

> The British Weather
> British Weather plc
> BritWeather
>
> To register your interest call for a FREE share information pack NOW!

The above public service announcement is part of an ongoing awareness campaign that's already cost the taxpayer £34m (+VAT) and counting. £34m (+VAT) may seem a lot of money, but it's nothing compared with the cost of person-hours lost to the British economy through a Sudden Cold Snap. This fact makes Weather Forecasting the key to our economic recovery in the 1990s – and a very nice little earner for the Enterprising Bluffer. You too could move in next door to Mrs T some day, if you stick at it and eat up all your potatoes.

We are, of course, very lucky in our weather. At the North Pole, for instance, you'd be lucky if 'unchangeable, with long cold periods lasting well into the millennium' didn't pretty well sum it up for all time (but see **Global Warming**).

At the other extreme, large deserts only enjoy rain about once every two years. This means that the odds against getting a cheerful forecast right are 730-1.

There are no two ways about it: we British are very lucky in our weather, and we are doubly fortunate in our weather forecasters. With the sort of weather forecasters we've got, there's plenty of scope for the other 56 million of us.

Being a Weather Forecaster

People often ask me (A Lobotomist writes) 'How do I become a Weather Forecaster?' The answer, sadly, is Deeply Depressing. First, you have to be a highly qualified, grossly over-worked and grotesquely under-funded Meteorologist. This is very hard, and involves years of training. It is not recommended for decent, right-minded slobs like you and me, mostly because it has the effect of making people terribly, terribly boring.

Next, you have to be selected. A tedium contest is held. Ordinary people are dragged in off the street and subjected to hours of witty chit-chat at the hands of fully qualified Meteorologists. After a while only one ordinary member of the public is left not chewing his or her own feet off in brain-dead exasperation. Thus, a winner emerges.

He or she (they both look the same) is then acclaimed Meteorologist Of The Year, given a pair of silly glasses and one of Russ Abbott's cast-off jackets, and shoved in front of a TV camera to become a Boring Personality for ever after and appear on the cover of the *Radio Times* twice every three years.

(Radio weather forecasters, on the other hand, are chosen for the impenetrability of their regional accents.)

So better forget about being real weather forecasters. Being weather bluffers, though, is quite another matter altogether: for once the sky is, literally, the limit.

Let's face it, you know you can do it – especially if you happened to be in the south of England on October 16th 1987. And the fact of the matter is of course that you can – bluff, that is, which is all the real ones do anyway.

Bluffer's Tip: Fahrenheit

Weather forecasters HATE Fahrenheit. This is because it's a nice, homely, accurate way of measuring temperature. They prefer Centigrade (which they call Celsius because they think it makes them sound sophisticated. You may call it Kelvin, but never Kevin – it's not worth knowing that intimately). Centigrade is, as every right-thinking person knows, a nasty, brutish, crude, Teutonic sort of measurement. It's like making love with boxing gloves on. Eschew it.

THE BASICS

Weather Forecasting, like Roman Gaul, is divided into Three Parts, viz:

> WHY does Weather happen?
> HOW does Weather happen?
> WHAT exactly is going to happen?

Meteorologists are very good at the WHY and the HOW. So good, in fact, that it would be pointless trying to compete with them; anyone who does is not a bluffer at all, but a nitwit.

Our concern is, of course, with the WHAT. And to this end never forget:

The Golden Rule.
> The Golden Rule is simple:

> *** NEVER COMMIT YOURSELF ***

> The words 'will' and 'won't' are *out*.
> The words 'can', 'may', 'could', 'might' and especially 'should' are *in*.

That's it. It's as simple as that. Honestly; no bluffing.

Having duly acknowledged that the WHY and the HOW of weather are best left to the professionals, it would be as well to have a quick look at them before going on to the real meat of the WHAT. You never know, you might find yourself in a tight corner (like trying to chat up a Meteorologist at a party) and have a desperate need to flannel your way out of it.

WHY?

All our weather comes from the oceans, which are very low down, and some really quite extraordinarily strong winds, which are very high up and which blow all the time, even when you're not riding a bicycle. The oceans evaporate moisture which condenses and cools as it rises and, shifted about by the strong winds, falls as rain, especially during the Headingly Test.

These winds do not blow in nice, decent, reliable straight lines however. They wiggle. On a diagram they look like a mass of half-cooked tagliatelle (here's some we prepared earlier) trying to strangle the globe. In real life you can't see them at all, which is very metaphysical and downright sneaky of them.

There are two things to remember about these winds:

1. **They are Utterly Reliable.**
   They have good, solid, traditional British names like the North-East Trades and the Prevailing Westerlies (Cap'n, art thou sleeping there below?)

2. **They are Utterly Unreliable.**
   This is partly due to the rotation of the Earth, which produces something called the Coriolis Force and which you may call the Tagliatelle Effect, and partly due to Chaos (see **Chaos**).

They are a sort of last ditch excuse for Meteorobluffers. "Ah, well," you say, "the Tagliatelle Effect, very unpredictable," and shake your head sadly. It's usually quite safe (but mostly wrong) to refer to them collectively as The Jet Stream; it sounds highly technocratic, like the phrase 'market forces' as used by politicians.

It's now time to introduce the word **Atmosphere**. As well as being something caused by eating too much Belgian paté at a party, the Atmosphere is something you may safely mention whenever you run out of inspiration or British Sauterne-Type. This is partly because it's from the Greek words αγμοσ (= gas) and σφαιρα (= balls), both of which are, of course, essential to any half-way decent bluff. Mostly it's because the Atmosphere, so far as the weather is concerned, is where it all happens.

A really good diagram of the Atmosphere is a truly beautiful thing; the reality, these days, isn't so nice.

Starting at the top we have the Exosphere, where nothing much happens and no-one can hear you scream.

Next down is the Thermosphere, which is handy for keeping picnic drinks in. This is where the Aurora Borealis happens, a peculiar astro-meteorological effect brought on by living too long in Aberdeen.

Next comes the Mesopause (which is treatable with hormone replacement therapy) and the Mesosphere, which is where Very Secret US spy planes live.

(Taken together, the Exosphere, the Thermosphere and the Mesosphere account for 93 per cent of the volume of the Atmosphere, but they only account for 1 per cent of its mass. Most of this 1 per cent is composed of US spy planes and TV satellites. You may now forget you ever heard of them.)

Next down is the Stratosphere, where Concorde flies when it's got a really good head of steam up. This includes the Ozone Layer (see **Global Warming**) and several Boeing 747s, which probably explains a lot. Then there's the Tropopause (boring).

Now comes the Big One.

The **Troposphere** is 11km (6 miles or roughly the distance from Battersea Park to Kew Gardens) thick, and the lowest layer of all. It's where ALL the weather is. It's what we breathe and sneeze in. Its main constituents are oxygen, carbon dioxide and nitrogen but there are also significant amounts of chlorine, methane, inert gases (the remains of politicians' speeches), dandruff, fag ash, B.O., and biodegradable Greenpeace novelty balloons. It's usually got clouds in it (see **Clouds**) except in Southern California, where they'd be wasted.

Bluffer's Tip:

Never refer simply to The Weather.
Instead, always talk about Tropospheric Effects.

HOW?

You might think that the Weather (Tropospheric Activity) is brought to us by PowerGen. Not so. We are concerned only with the strictly kosher, BBC stuff. Our weather comes from CYCLONES and ANTICYCLONES. Cyclones very often have **Deep Depressions** in them; anticyclones are more cheerful, but tricky, and can when they're in the mood bring **Ridges Of High Pressure** (see *The Bluffer's Guide To Naughty Massage*). Both are absolutely bursting with Weather.

In summer, cyclones bring us wind and rain; in winter they bring us wind, rain and Scattered Wintry Showers, Prolonged In Places.

In summer, anticyclones produce spells of fine, warm, dry weather (except in the Northern Isles) and occasional fog. In winter they produce cold, watery sunshine (especially at high tide), frost, and a lot more fog.

Note:
The M6 between junctions 21 and 26 in Greater Manchester is *always* foggy, even when it's raining. This is called Transport Planning.

Cyclones and anticyclones (when meteorologists get really stuck they tend to call them Complex Weather Systems) are attended by hangers-on called Cold Fronts (Margaret Thatcher), Warm Fronts (the Queen Mother) and Occluded Fronts (Myra Breckenridge).

We'll come back to all this later on; it's time to get down to . . .

WHAT?

To be a Real Bluffer is to be concerned solely with Empiric Systems (© the late Bertrand Russell). Empirically speaking, this means: try anything once and if it works, do it again. Empirical Thinking has given us the cat flap, the bouncing bomb and the ball-cock, so don't knock it. All truly human weather forecasters are Empiricists, but daren't admit it. You, as a bluffer, are an Empiricist *and proud of it*. Never forget that, especially at really good parties.

There are as many ancient systems of Empirical weather forecasting as there are freebooting con-artists, which is to say, a hell of a lot. These include:

Seaweed. Hang up some seaweed. If it becomes wet and slimy, it's raining. If it becomes dry and crackly, you've hung it up indoors.

Fruit in Hedgerows. Lack of fruit in hedgerows (blackberries, raspberries, red berêts, beri-beris, etc.) was said to indicate a short, mild winter OR a good prospect for next year's Headingly Test. These days it's more likely to indicate that your local council's got trigger-happy with the herbicide.

Migrating Birds. Late departure of migrating birds (swifts, swoops, sweeps, stormy termagents, Pamella Bordes, etc.) is alleged to augur a complete change in the weather pattern brought on by Complex Frontal Systems (e.g. Hot Gossip). Actually it's because they booked with a cowboy travel agent.

Comforting Couplets: For instance,
'Red sky at night, Chernobyl's alight;
Red sky in the morning, global warming.'

And so on, and on, and on. Any bluffer who can't invent his/her own Ancient Portents doesn't deserve to be in the frame to start with. You should bear in mind the Old Countryman's Maxim:

'When goats and milkmaids do lie down together
'neath the shade of an oak or upas tree on the
night of a full moon when the wind is in the
south-west and there's an r in the month, they
do say: Anything Might Happen.'

Some people, especially NHS patients, claim they can tell the weather by their arthritis: when it hurts, it's wet and when it hurts like hell it's dry and sunny because they've been out for a walk in it. Or there is the case of the lady who wrote to the papers to say she could always tell when it was going to snow by the behaviour of her tits in the garden. You could try pretending that you can predict the state of the weather by the state of your libido. Just make sure you've made a thoroughly accurate assessment of the person you're talking to first.

All this semi-superstitious stuff might be all right for sociologists but it's not enough for us. What we need is a good, reliable supply of . . .

QUASI-SCIENTIFIC WEATHERY THINGS

These are a real comfort and no mistake. Used judiciously, they should see you through the first three hours of a railway journey, after which you'll have the carriage to yourself. The two quasi-scientific weathery things (quastwats) of particular interest to you are **clouds**, and **wind**.

CLOUDS

Clouds are wonderful. Everyone knows they're there; hardly anyone knows what they are; nobody, except Meteorologists, is privy to all their Eleusinian Mysteries (see *The Bluffer's Guide To The Classics*). Neither are you, of course, but here's how to fake it.

First you should learn that clouds occur in three layers of the Troposphere, very boringly named the Upper Layer, the Middle Layer, and the All-Night Acid House Party Layer. No, that's silly; it's called the Lower Layer.

Secondly, they come in three broad categories:

- **Clouds of Instability** (schizophrenics)
- **Clouds of Limited Instability** (professional authors)
- **Clouds of Stability** (chartered accountants).

Those marked with an asterisk (*, if you're a clot) are particularly recommended.

Cumulus

Low-to-middle. Unstable, but quite attractively so, like the pretty girl at the party whom all the men have forgiven for putting her mother in a Home. Cumulus looks like cotton-wool and comes in two flavours, viz:

1. **Cumulus Humilis** (Ever-so-'umble Cumulus) which is white and fluffy, often flat at the bottom and protuberant at the top. One Real Weather book describes it as 'burgeoning not unlike cauliflower curds'. You, who have more imagination, can do better than that. Think of cloud-capp'd towers, Henry Moore sculptures, Sumo wrestlers, etc. They are quite harmless (the clouds, that is) and mean it won't rain, only you must remember to say 'shouldn't', of course.

2. **Cumulus mediocris** (Dirty Rat Cumulus) or **congestus** (Gob Cumulus)*. This is Cumulus gone to the bad, a cloud that's kept unsavoury company. It's much bigger than the nice stuff, and grey-black at the bottom. It thrusts very rude-looking bits of itself into the upper layer in a thoroughly offensive and chauvinistic manner. It precedes a cold wind, and usually showers as well, and is well worth abandoning a picnic for, especially if there's something good on television.

Cumulonimbus*

Middle-to-upper layer, and unstable verging on the barking mad. Traditionally described as 'anvil-shaped' but few people know what an anvil is these days. Think instead of the National Theatre. That is to say, it's enormous, filthy, wider at the top than at the bottom and monstrously ugly. Forecast gale force winds (see **Wind**) blowing from 'unpredictable directions' and lots of heavy rain (in winter, Wintry Downpours). If you can hear crackling on your Long Wave radio, forecast thunderstorms as well.

Bluffer's Tip: thunder and lightning (sturm und drang). We all know about counting 'one-two-three' after the lightning and then, when we hear the thunder, saying how far away the storm is. This is not good enough. Count 'one thousand – two thousand – three thousand . . .' to get the distance in kilometers. Count 'one banana – two banana – three banana . . .' to get it in miles. This is incredibly inaccurate but very impressive. Remember thunderstorms move in spirals (the Tagliatelle Effect, probably) so don't make rash predictions about where it's going or when it will appear overhead. Remember that all sheet lightning (ordinary) is merely forked lightning (exciting) too far away to see properly. This is rubbish, but cannot be disproved at the time.

Cirrocumulus (high), Altocumulus (middle) and Stratocumulus (low)

All these clouds are relatively stable and comparatively unstable (lots of mileage there) and each is a rather tedious variation of the other. The first two are the most promising from our point of view (e.g. the kitchen window).

Cirrocumulus* (not to be confused with *cirrhobibulus*, which is alcoholic degeneration of the liver) looks like small white shiny fish scales and is sometimes called a 'mackerel sky'. It looks very pretty, especially at sunset with a large dry sherry. It always presages CHANGE (as does everything else, of course, including the sherry). Whatever the weather is now, say it probably won't be tomorrow. And why not? It's your booze.

Altocumulus* is the same (or if you live in Somerset, the zame) only bigger and lower down. "My, my," you say, "I can certainly see a change in the weather coming on. Altocumulus, quite unmistakeable. Oh thanks, just a small one then."

16

Stratocumulus is deadly dull: dirty great slabs of grey-white-pus coloured filth, very low down. They mean drizzle, except when they mean rain, but never a White Christmas. Go indoors for another bottle.

Cirrus

White, very high up and moving at very high speed, which is why they often look like go-faster lines in a cartoon strip (or, to be traditional, mares'-tails). Surprisingly – but not particularly interestingly – they are stable clouds. They mean you're having fine weather (obviously, or you couldn't see them) but probably mean change in two-three days' time, i.e. rain. Probably. If not sooner.

Cirrostratus

Not to be confused with Cirrosmith, MP for Rochdale (fog). This is the high, stable, very thin cloud ('gossamer-thin' if kids are out of earshot) that always spoils outings to the beach. This is because it gives the illusion of full sunlight while at the same time raising goose-pimples on your exposed flesh because it's just thick enough to absorb all the heat that's rightfully yours. Abandon all thoughts of toplessness (but not your top) and play a jolly game of beach cricket instead, the kiddies (who haven't got tops and don't feel the cold) will love it.

It is said that a halo 22° across can be measured round the sun in these conditions by holding your hand out at arm's length towards the sun and looking at it. Not recommended, especially if you've got long arms: looking at the sun (like reading the *Sun*) can make you blind.

Altostratus

As Cirrostratus, only lower and thicker (like *Sun* readers). Old Meteorological Bores will tell you you can still get nasty sunburn through it. They should be so

17

lucky. A typical Scottish Tourist Board cloud. Sometimes brings a few spots of rain if it can be bothered.

Nimbostratus

Not to be confused with Limbostratus, which is where you go when you die, though it's not a bad comparison. An absolute dead loss, this one: bloody-mindedly stable and throat-cuttingly low, it looks like used plasticine and spreads for hundreds of miles, just like radiation from Sellafield doesn't. It sometimes has small, very black clouds scudding about underneath it. It makes you put your lights on to get your mid-morning gin. It chucks it down. Tell family and friends the best you can hope for is a breakdown of this particular frontal system sometime before the end of the holiday. Then get on with your own breakdown.

Stratus

Simple. When all you can see is cloud, it's this one. Brings rain/drizzle/hail/granulated snow/unwanted junk mail, depending on your credit rating. Go back to bed.

Orographic Cloud***

Only occurs round high mountains in God's Own Country, i.e. the Scottish Highlands. (Readers in Wales have their own weather; see **Nimbostratus**). Looks like a smoke ring or an illustration from a Tolkein book. Utterly charming. Pretend to have seen one round Nelson's Column.

Turbofanulocumulonimbulus*****

High up, and a sort of magnolia colour, just right for the bathroom. Quite straight and varying in width. Can be used to forecast *absolutely anything*, including giant

Venusian frogs. This is because it's the decaying vapour-trail of a jet, but don't let on.

WIND

> 'Blow, blow, thou winter wind,
> Thou art not so unkind
> As man's ingratitude.'

Shakespeare: As You Lump It

Whereas clouds may be used (between consenting adults, except in Ulster) to forecast the weather just before it happens (sometimes), **wind** can only be employed in an effort to be wise during the event. Since being w. during the e. constitutes 98 per cent of conversations about the weather, that's fine by you.

Winds are rated from 0 to 12 on the Beaufort Scale, which was orginally devised to help sailors. Thus a Force 4 comes out as 'small waves becoming longer; more frequent white horses'. This is no use if you live in Birmingham (nothing is, really) and besides, it's time for a word of

Warning:

Never try to bluff your way round weather forecasting with Oceanic types of person. They are not suitable material for bluffers, especially:

Yachtsmen (Luffers) – definitely to be shunned unless you're wearing the right sort of blazer. (If female, the right sort of wet-look T-shirt and glass of Martini Rosso).

Fishermen (Gaffers) – avoid like the plague unless you're passionately interested in EC halibut quotas.

Royal Navy Officers (Sniftahs) – likely to think that the weather is something that goes *ping* on a computer screen; might as well be Meteorologists.

Besides, Oceanic types have an arrogant and outrageous habit of thinking they Know It All; worse still, they sometimes do.

Here, then, completely gratis, is a:

Revised Beaufort Scale

0	Dead Calm	Dead, as in exhaust fumes (town) or pesticide (country).
1	Light air	Your cigarette annoys an anti-smoking Reichsmarshal half a mile downwind on Salisbury Plain.
2	Light breeze	Your children play dandelion clocks all over your freshly-weeded flowerbeds.
3	Gentle breeze	McDonalds wrappers move about but do not blow away. Next door's drains say hello.
4	Moderate breeze	At an open-air meeting in Kirkubrightshire Dr David Owen forecasts an SDP revival.
5	Fresh breeze	Suddenly the street is full of Marilyn Monroe lookalikes. Men arrested for looking.
6	Strong breeze	McDonalds wrappers blow into your garden. Your train home is 28 mins late 'owing to wet leaves at Norbury'.

7	Near gale	Time to take the dog for a walk. People in Orkney say 'Better weather today, isn't it!'
8	Gale	Postman Pat's hat blows off for the 358th time on TV. Windsurfers cause 5-mile jam on the M25.
9	Strong gale	End of civilisation south of Watford. First half of *Nine o'Clock News* devoted to broken chimney pots in Surrey.
10	Storm	People in Orkney hang their sheets out and mow the lawn.
11	Violent storm	The Archbishop of Canterbury says the Pope might be a little bit infallible after all.
12	Hurricane	Your house insurance premium goes up. The TV goes off. Your friendly corner shop sells candles at £1.50 each.

ABSOLUTELY SCIENTIFIC WEATHERY THINGS

This is where you must not be faint-hearted. Remember that weather forecasting is like palmistry: a man can always tell a woman's Line of Venus is very strong by the way she grasps his hand and smothers it with passionate kisses. You can always say something intelligent about your subject's Line of Emphysema if it ends in a large nicotine stain ... and so on. Weather forecasting is no different: it's a simple matter of reading between the isobars.

It's time to face up to Weather Systems.

There are, fortunately, only two of these worth bothering about.

Cyclones

These are areas of **low pressure**, that is to say of low air pressure as measured at sea level. Joining up the various identical measurements of air pressure gives you lines called **isobars** which are like contour lines on a map, only measured at 5 millibar intervals (don't worry about these) instead of in metres (or, if you're a True Blue Brit, feet). Air pressure used to be measured in inches of mercury, which has now been banned as a sop to the Green Party and withdrawn from supermarket shelves after becoming contaminated with battery chicken. When all these lines are drawn you get something that looks like a lot of concentric fried eggs. This is called a **cyclone**.

Cyclones are windy things. The closer together the isobars, the stronger the wind. And the wind in a cyclone ALWAYS travels ANTICLOCKWISE*. The other won-

* But see **Southern Hemisphere**

derful thing about cyclones is that they ALWAYS COME FROM THE WEST (bad luck if you live in Stornoway). Armed with this information you should always know, roughly, how strong the wind will be and where it'll come from. Roughly speaking, the further east you go across Britain the less violent the wind will be (if it's coming from the left hand side) and the less rain will fall. As the cyclone moves away, the wind will come round to blow from the right hand side and the east coast will cop it. Roughly. When you see a lot of isobars all packed very close together it probably means a hurricane – but don't tell the met men. It's a secret.

In front of nearly every cyclone is ('should be', remember) a Warm Front, shown as a line with bumps on. This means lots of rain. As the cyclone moves away it usually brings in a Cold Front (shown as a line with triangles on). This means cooler, brighter weather with frequent showers, heavy in places (and, in winter, Wintry.)

Cyclones always come from the west, as we've said, and are sometimes referred to as 'deep depressions centred in mid-Atlantic'. So would you be deeply depressed, if you were. Mid Atlantic is even more boring than hospital.

Very occasionally, cyclones move back again from the east to have another go. Your sense of outrage on these occasions will know no bounds.

Anticyclones

These are just the same as cyclones, i.e. they have isobars, but they are areas of high pressure and the winds (usually light) in them always travel CLOCKWISE*. Also, they don't usually come from the west; sometimes it's the south-west and often it's the south, almost invariably the Azores (where you met that ghastly couple from Crawley

* But see **Southern Hemisphere**

23

last holidays). Strangely enough, for bringers of fine weather, they're often associated with Cold Fronts. (See **HOW?** to remind yourselves what anticyclones do for us.)

Sometimes both **cyclones** and **anticyclones** can bring Occluded Fronts (shown as lines with bumps and triangles on). These are crazy, mixed-up areas of warm and cold air. The weather in these circumstances is always VERY CHANGEABLE, leading to scattered showers of volcanic ash in Whitehall.

Bluffer's Tip: Denmark

Forget all you've heard about Denmark being an unamusing, social democratic sort of place. When you've read the following paragraph you'll be knocking back the Carlsberg and raising your smørgasbørd in honour of those plucky little Legolanders.

A High Pressure (Anticyclone) area situated over Denmark in the summer *and staying there* means LOTS AND LOTS OF LOVELY HOT FINE WEATHER (except in the Northern Isles). This is because it sort of fends off all those suicidal mid-Atlantic depressions, shoving them up to Iceland and down to France, where they belong.

What it does for the Danes is not recorded.

Since the whole point of being a Meteorobluffer is to switch off the television weather forecast after a two-second glance at the chart and say, "Oh well, that's this weekend's outing off, then," or "Darling, why don't we go out in the country tomorrow, just the two of us?" (or whatever), *who could ask for more?*

And even if you did, you're not getting it from us. Any more detailed information than this and you might turn into a Meteorobore. Worse still, so might we.

The Southern Hemisphere – A Warning

A remarkable achievement of the Coriolis Force and the Tagliatelle Effect is to cause all the Weather south of the equator to go the other way round. This has various meteorological effects, e.g. anticyclones travel counter-clockwise, cyclones travel anticounterclockwise, Ramsay Street has British summers and department store Father Christmases collapse from heatstroke. This is a result of Global Rotation and is proved by micrometer measurement of the Sydney-Goolagong railway line, which shows that the left hand rail is always slightly more worn than the right hand one; this is quite different from Britain, where both are closed due to Granulated Snow at Redhill.

Unfortunately certain other Weathery Things are just the same: Depressions are just as depressing; in the case of Canberra and large areas of suburban New Zealand, even more so. This is known as the Melbourne Phenomenon, the effects of which are carried right round the planet by the all-pervasive **Minogue**, causing massive algal blooms of *Kiwitekanawa* and allowing eco-threatening satellite TV stations to penetrate the Ozone Layer.

The **Minogue** is Australia's answer to European winds like the Mistral, the Sirrocco, the Sierra, the Polski-Fiat, etc. It is a devastatingly vacuous current of stale air which, once it has invaded a climatic system, is almost impossible to get rid of; it pops up all over the place, especially where it has no apparent right to be, and drives normal people insane with its incessant twangy whining. It is particularly prevalent in areas exposed to the *Sun*, and the only reliable method of protection is to wrap up well with copies of the *New Scientist* and tune to Radio 3.

Antipodean Weather is further complicated by large amounts of Perfectly Harmless (*perfectement inoffensif*) French Radiation (*la tombée atomique de la gloire Française*) released into the Ozzisphere from a number of South Pacific Islands in an attempt to destabilise the

Commonweather, thereby forcing Britain to join the **EMS** and submit to the diktat of the European Community's Sunny Period Commissioner. This particular meteorological *Pomme Chaud* must now be considered.

The European Meteorological System

The European Meteorological System (EMS) or, as it is sometimes called, the ERM (*l'Echange Raisonable Meteorologique*) was the brainchild of M. Michel Poisson and his associates in the European Weather Centre at Bracknell-les-deux-Eglises. Put at its simplest (that is to say, in terms even a British Prime Minister may readily misinterpret) it is an agreement whereby the various weather systems of the Community can be harmonised, consolidated and held within rigidly ill-defined guidelines in time to meet the challenge of the Single European Climate in 1992. Eleven of the twelve EC members have so far joined – hence its nickname, the *Onze Temps Cordial* – but Britain still remains outside.

Opponents of the EMS point out that the rest of Europe (except Eire, which doesn't count) has a Continental Climate with hot dry summers (bare breasts, olive oil, rabies, cheap wine and scattered lagerlouts) and cold winters (Brueghel skating scenes made into difficult jigsaws, Alps, and the 7.50 from Three Bridges to Victoria cancelled due to frozen points in Schleswig-Holstein).

The British Climate, on the other hand, is Temperate – that is to say, Reasonable, Moderate, and Infinitely Changeable; rough winds do shake the darling buds of May they point out (especially in the Northern Isles) and Autumn is the season of mists, mellow fruitfulness, and 15-mile tailbacks on the M6 in Greater Manchester.

To alter this in favour of some half-baked scheme to turn Aberdeen into the St Tropez of the North would, they say, threaten the very sovereignty of the British Weather and undermine the Mid-Atlantic Depression to the extent of wiping out the Scottish Parka Industry. Furthermore, it is argued, the flotation of BritWeather could be an even bigger flop than Electricity, leading to an embarrassing two-minute silence after the *Nine O'Clock News* and a re-introduction of the Interlude.

Finally, they warn, the admission of Turkey to full EC membership would have a devastatingly adverse impact on the vital Tory marginals of Sunny Clacton and Seasonally Adjusted Skegness.

Despite this opposition, it is known that senior influential weather forecasters favour early entry and a renegotiation of the terms agreed (by Britain, with eleven against) at the Bad Handbäg Summit. These are:

1. A free market in Complex Weather Patterns;
2. A Quota System for Mid-Atlantic Depressions, ensuring that all member countries agree to take their share of wet Augusts;
3. A cast-iron guarantee from the Bundesbanke that the Germans won't always get to the beach first;
4. The US to be allowed to go on deploying Cold Front Weather Systems at Greenham Common;
5. The maintenance of a Meteorological Exclusion Zone round the Northern Isles until they stop voting Liberal.

Wrangling over EMS membership came to a head recently when the Prime Minister's part-time Weather Adviser published an article in the *Mid-Ohio Drizzle Quarterly* in which he described the scheme as 'utterly occluded'. This led to the resignation of the Secretary of State for Seasonal Adjustments, who saw his complex frontal system breaking down under transatlantic high pressure, and calls from backbench government forecasters for the rapid implementation of long, hot summers in their constituencies in time for the next election.

SHORT-TERM BLUFFING

(What d'you reckon for this morning, then?)

Sun

Sun comes in various doses; starting with the smallest these are: sunny intervals, sunny spells, sunny periods, prolonged sunny periods and (hardly ever) prolonged periods of unbroken sunshine. It's best to stick to the middle range (© Dr David Owen). The key word is LUCKY, as in:

"We'll be lucky to have any sun this morning, I reckon."

This sounds as though you're being realistic. You're vindicated if you're right, forgotten if you're wrong.

And: "I reckon we'll be unlucky not to see *some* sunshine."

This sounds cheerful, which is what a bluffer should be. Full marks if correct, forgiveness and fellow-feeling all round if you're not.

There's no accounting for luck, after all.

Rain

Rain (or British Precipitation Enterprises plc as it's now called) is caused by warm moist air rising, being driven over cold air and/or cold land, and falling as water droplets. (Hence the expression, 'droppeth as the gentle Wintry Shower from heaven'.) When warm moist air hits high mountains it drops the lot; this is why Aberdeen is drier (but colder) than Skye – mind you: who on earth, apart from Texans with thermal underwear, would want to live in Aberdeen? Bear this in mind, then look at the clouds (see **Clouds**).

Amounts of rain:

Drizzle, light showers, scattered showers, squally showers, heavy showers, prolonged periods of heavy rain and (especially during Wimbledon) continuous heavy rain but becoming drier towards midnight with renewed showers around Dawn, who's still waiting for her bus home.

Remember that rain falls when warm air moves over cold ground, and bear in mind that the ground is always colder at night (big light in sky go out, tee vee he say time for adult programmes). This is why it's often fine when you go to bed but lousy when you.wake up, especially if you're morally unsound.

The key word with rain is SURPRISED, as in:

"I'll be surprised if this rain doesn't let up."
And: "It wouldn't surprise me if we had some rain later on."

Fog

Remember that High Pressure (Anticyclone) conditions always bring the risk, sorry, opportunity, of fog, especially in winter (especially in the Northern Isles).

You have a choice of three types of fog:

1. **Advection Fog**
   This is caused by our old chum, the mass of warm air (the TUC) passing over a cold surface (the DSS) and is very common at sea, especially in Winter. A useful tip for Winterbreak Weekends in Scarborough, if you're daft enough to have them.

2. **Radiation Fog** (Chernobylonimbus)
   Land fog, caused by warm, etc., etc., and lingering in low places (Hamburg Otto's Wine'n'Nipple Bar, Oldham) in the morning.

Both these fogs look the same, of course – or rather, don't –
especially between junctions 21 and 26 of the M6, and in
the Forth-Clyde Valley.

3. **Freezing Fog**
    Caused by warm air, cold fronts, high pressure,
    inflationary wage claims, a slippage in the Yen, a
    blip in the trade figures and the complete failure
    of Britain's post-war planning and/or Tony Benn.
    Join the AA.

Snow

Snow is just rain you buy at Derry & Thoms, and vastly
overrated especially in British Sherry commercials. The
reason (you will say) that it hardly ever snows cats and
dogs (like it rains) is because Warm Fronts (*Emmanuelle
I-VIII* incl.) are too warm for snow to happen. (It's ice, you
see.)

Snow, therefore, tends to come in Showers (some of
them Heavy and Prolonged) on the back end of a
Depression (have you tried gin and Esso? It makes
Depressions really memorable). Snow is particularly
likely on high ground (e.g. the Cuillins in June) and, you'll
be glad to hear, in Birmingham. Snow is quite a novelty in
the Northern Isles; when it does fall there it always has
the effect of cancelling the 6.40 from Haywards Heath to
London Bridge (the Super Shoveller).

Never promise snow to children. Hold out the vague
offer of Wintry Showers instead; they have to learn that
this weary old world of ours is a cruel and disappointing
place. Then, when it *does* snow cats and dogs for two whole
days and nights you can say you Knew It All Along but
Wanted It To Be A Surprise. With any luck they'll be so
grateful they'll agree on the spot to tithe their incomes in
your favour when you're old and crumbly.

Hail

Hail was always as big as golf balls in your grandfather's day. It's odd stuff, hail. It can fall at any time of year, for no sensible reason at all, and is impossible to forecast without a large European Community subsidy (known in Brussels as a *Zut Delors*). When it does fall, point out that in 1789 two people were killed in Buckinghamshire by a fall of jagged ice crystals up to eight inches long – in July. It's true. Then start remembering your grandfather.

Frost

There are two sorts of frost:

1. **Air frost**. When the air above the ground is below freezing, you get air frost (the Xmas Card Effect). This is bad for tender plants, your car radiator which you forgot to put Austrian wine in, and Poor Baby's Tender Little Cheeks. Put plastic bags over all of them from November-March – but remember, some plants can suffocate easily.

2. **Ground Frost**. Obvious, really. Postpone all garden digging until January, when with a bit of luck you won't be able to do it.

Professional forecasters usually forecast frost in two sorts of area, which are easily adaptable even if they don't apply to your neighbourhood. They are:

Sheltered Inland Areas (= Birmingham City FC);
Remote Highland Glens (= next door's open cold frame).

Forecast frost with complete confidence whenever there's

31

a clear sky on a winter evening. You will often be completely wrong. When this happens, go out into the garden next morning, prod the ground with your fingers and say:

"Ah! An overnight job, all gone by dawn. Thought so."
It never fails, unless you've married someone intelligent.

Bluffer's Tip: The Northern Isles

As a dedicated Meteorobluffer you will keep in touch with Meteorobores via the medium of Radio 4; television weather forecasts are just kids' stuff. You will therefore be familiar with the phrase '... except in the Northern Isles', which usually follows the promise of 'bright, dry, fine sunny weather'. This is because the Northern Isles really belong to Norway (or Denmark) and they must NEVER on any account be referred to as 'the Orkneys and Shetlands' because they aren't. They have their own mini-climates, comprising two seasons:

- Summer (May 15th – Aug 20th or County Show Day in Kirkwall, whichever is the sooner)
- Winter;

and two sorts of weather:

1. cool, windy and wet;
2. cool, windy and foggy.

Book now: they'll be THE place to be when East Anglia turns into a desert. This brings us nicely to . . .

GLOBAL WARMING

Do not be put off by all the awful warnings about Global Warming: they are just scare stories put about by desperate weather men frightened of losing their jobs and hell-bent on subverting our Economic Recovery, which as we all know lies a tantalising sixteen Tory governments away.

Nothing terrifies them more than Global Warming (except possibly **Chaos**) because they know that if it ever works out the way the eco-fundamentalists predict, they'll be out of a job because anyone's guess will be as good as theirs.

You, of course, already know this is true.

Don't be complacent, though. Fill your leisure hours by scouring the supermarket shelves for CFC aerosols, smashing up old fridges and converting your Wartburg to run on leaded coal and old washing-up bottles. Every little helps.

The glorious factoid (= an opinion that proves things are the way you want them to be) about Global Warming is that it's the best thing that's happened to bluffers since the overthrow of Keynesian economics. It only goes to show that if there is a God, he's One Of Us (see **Chaos**).

The basic facts of Global Warming are very simple (even the *Daily Mail* gets them right) and, as such, of no interest to us because 98 per cent of people at parties already know them. However, for the same reason, it is vital to set them out yet again. Running sparkling rings round people at parties is, after all, what you've been put on Earth to do and you can't pervert the truth unless you know what it is.

Briefly, then:

The Ozone Layer

Just above the Troposphere (where the Weather is) and the Tropopause (where it isn't) is the Stratosphere (remember?), so called after the Greek word for bloody high up.

The Stratosphere is about 30 miles thick (or, if you're thinking of popping over to the Continent for the weekend, 50km). The bottom bit of it contains the Ozone Layer, whose function is to filter out quite a lot of the Sun's ultraviolet radiation. Radiation, remember, is either Very Harmful or Utterly Safe, depending on whether you're publicity director of British Nuclear Fuels. Exhaustive tests on millionaire geriatrics in Florida have proved conclusively that it can cause skin cancer in rats and may in extreme cases lead to what doctors call Blimey, Have You Seen Next Door's Holiday Tan Syndrome.

Radiation from the Sun is, of course, what keeps us warm (except in the Northern Isles). Normally, a lot of this radiation – well, 26 per cent of it, which is a hell of a lot if you're in the SDP – bounces back out into space (especially from the Northern Isles) off the clouds (see **Clouds**) and the ground (see between your feet).

The Ozone Layer now has holes in it, mostly because a lot of very selfish people will insist on spraying themselves with Odour-O-No.

These holes let more radiation in, and we all get warmer – all of us! Sunbathers in Shetland unzip their parkas. Good news, you may say as you rush out to build a 20-storey luxury hotel in Muckle Flugga. BUT. . .

The Greenhouse Effect

A lot of nonsense is talked about the Greenhouse Effect, but don't despair: there is always room for more. The

Greenhouse Effect – in which that 26 per cent of the Sun's radiation (allowing for Don't Knows and Scottish Nationalists) bounces back but fails to continue out into space to fuel the Star Wars Program – is caused by a build-up in the Atmosphere (look up) of carbon dioxide (bad breath) and methane (cow farts), but mostly carbon dioxide (CO_2) because methane's more fun.

Carbon dioxide traps the radiation and holds it in the Atmosphere, *thus making it warmer still*. Better add another 10 storeys to that hotel: the population will need somewhere to go when the polar ice goes critical.

It is vitally important to remember that what leaks in through the Ozone String Vest is **ultraviolet** radiation and that what bounces back is called **infrared** radiation. Why? Because:

- it's true;
- not many people know it, especially at parties, and
- it prepares the ground for all the persuasive nonsense you're about to tell them.

First, let us remind ourselves that this build-up of CO_2 is caused by many things, and not just the ones we all know about, such as factory chimneys. Anything that produces the stuff is Bad, e.g:

- Passive smokers asserting their right to breathe;
- 'Attunement' at Green Party conferences;
- Unleaded petrol conversion kit salesmen;
- Dan Quayle;
- Satellite television;
- Next door's dog;
- Weather Forecasters;
- Cecil Parkinson;
- Lager;
- Life, Liberty and the Pursuit of Happiness;
- Sex (except in the Northern Isles).

35

But what, we hear you cry, has all this got to do with weather forecasting? Gentle reader, why do you think they call these things Bluffer's Guides? They pay by the yard for this stuff.

But if you insist, it's this:

Effects of Global Warming on the Weather

The space above has been left blank for you to write your own ideas.

This is because the fact of the matter is:
NOBODY KNOWS.

But weather forecasters, to cloak their ignorance, suggest that:

1. Very Hot Places will get Even Hotter. (This doesn't concern us, as we're British.)
2. Very Cold Places will thaw out a bit. (Bad luck Arthur Scargill.)
3. Nice, sensible, in-between sort of easy-going places (such as the venue for this really most agreeable party) will *CHANGE UTTERLY* (or not).

For instance, you will say: imagine what the average garden in (wherever you are) could look like, post-warming ... mangoes, mangroves, womangroves, upas trees, alfafa, Al-Fayed, alcohol, algae *(Kiwitekanawa grandifulgus)*, rice, cacti, sewage-enriched plankton, Bull's Blood – oh, see what you mean, thanks old chap – melons the size of, that is to say, hello Angela . . . well, the rest is up to you.

This, you will eventually point out, is because an increase of only 1.3658239° Centigrade/Celsius/Kelvin (depending on the quality of the wine box, but never Kevin, who hasn't been invited, thank God), spread out over the lifetime of three Tory governments, can (never 'will', remember) have the most appallingly catastrophic effects on the Troposphere, the male Mesopause, the Thermosphlasque, AND THE WHOLE CLIMATIC SYSTEM (except in the Northern Isles).

NB!

1. Do not call it 'The Weather Machine' as this is considered terribly *passé*.
2. Do not call it 'The Climactic System'. If it was That Sort Of Party you wouldn't be talking about the weather.

If, armed with all these factoids, you cannot have the time of your life then you probably don't deserve to go to parties, anyway.

You might go on to point out that the single most important effect of Global Warming is that *more water evaporates into the Troposphere*. Use the homely analogy of boiling water in a saucepan to illustrate this. Or, if it's a posh do, remind your audience of the way fondue sort of goes all rubbery if it's not eaten quickly. Water evaporates up, and WHAT GOES UP MUST COME DOWN, HEAVILY (see **Deep Depressions**) ANYWHERE.

Top Meteorobores at the Mid Yell Tourist Office have already calculated that they could have 283 days of rain next year. This is wonderful news: last year they had 297.

37

Flooding

Though not strictly Weather, flooding caused by Global Warming is great bluff-fodder. Remind your listeners that we are an Island Race and, as such, subject to the biggest threat to the environment since Nicholas Ridley, viz: the sea.

Experts are vaguely agreed that with a 3 metre rise in sea levels anywhere within 40 miles of the coast (66km Sundays and Bank Holidays) is at risk, thus raising the prospect of Birmingham becoming the centre of British Civilisation. This is awful enough, but you don't have to stop there. Point out that Florida would disappear altogether.

There's no reason why any country you don't much care for shouldn't go the same way.

Or . . .

If you're going for the Bluffer's Black Belt, you could try dismissing the whole of the above as ARRANT NON-SENSE. ('Arrant' is a superb bluffer's word: nobody quite knows what it means but everybody thinks they ought to.) This is due to VARIOUS COUNTERVAILING COOLING EFFECTS (Vaccies, to the cognoscenti). These are, for starters:

1. **The Little Ice Age**. There is abundant evidence that we're about due for another of these (bad luck, Orkney and Shetland) and that a Frozen Front about 100 miles thick (DM2.85 or $1.58) will extend south to Torquay. (There's probably quite a lot of evidence that we aren't, but you don't need to know everything.)

2.   **Carbon dioxide is good for plants**. More CO_2 =
     more plants. More plants = more oxygen. (Plants
     breathe in CO_2 and breathe out O_2; humans do the
     opposite. Humans – with the exception of DTI fraud
     inspectors – are not cabbages.) More oxygen will
     counterbalance the carbon dioxide. Enough said.
     (This is more or less true, as far as it goes – which is
     quite far enough for you.)

3.   You happen to know something most people don't
     know about the Star Wars Program (about which
     nobody, especially George Bush, knows anything).

This sort of analysis is optimistic, hopeful, upbeat, good
for the Hang Seng Index, and almost completely irrele-
vant. It could well secure you a place in the next Cabinet.
It will certainly go down a treat at parties (except in parts
of Ulster and the Northern Isles).

SPACE – THE OCCLUDED FRONTIER

At any social gathering there comes the inevitable moment when even the most resourceful Meteorobluffer's fount of sparkling erudition threatens to dry up. You have discussed the effect of Global Warming on the Docklands Light Railway (and *vice-versa*); you have gauged the wind at Force 4, gusting to Force 8 through the cat-flap; you have exhausted all the conversational possibilities (all one of them) of Nimbostratus. Disaster looms in the form of your hosts' holiday airport departure lounge video unless you can come up with something scintillatingly Weathery.

This is where **Space** comes in.

We've already had a brief brush with the cosmos in our review of the Atmosphere. Beyond the Exosphere, where no-one can hear you bluff, lies the limitless kingdom/queendom/royal persondom/republic of the Enormosphere, which you may be tempted to think of as the Buggerallosphere. Resist the temptation. There's an awful lot of Weather out there, if you know where to look for it.

The Planets

Begin with the **planets**, since they're handy. There are at least nine of these, and some scientists believe that a proper understanding of what makes the other eight of them tick will prove to be the key to understanding many of Earth's meteorological problems, e.g. the Greenhouse Effect, the Mid-Atlantic Depression, the Minogue, the Orkney Summer, etc. This is Very Exciting.

Other scientists, however, believe that this sort of planetary study will turn out to be a complete waste of

40

time, space, and space-time. This is Utterly Thrilling.

More scientists insist that either theory – probably both – may well be true. This is called the SDP Space Policy and is the attitude recommended for Meteorobluffers. Bear in mind that it doesn't do to be too dogmatic, especially when it's so easy to be proved wrong, thus leaving no alternative but that awful video of the lost baggage.

First, you should mention the **Planetary Positions** relative to the Sun (but not the *Sun*, which would undoubtedly make a crude and feeble joke about the phrase 'planetary positions' and then run a Naughty Competition about them). Beginning at the Sun, then, the order is: Mercury, Venus, Earth, Mars, Jupiter, Saturn, Uranus, Neptune and Pluto (or, sometimes, Pluto and Neptune). This is easily learned with the help of the following mnemonic: Many Very Eccentric Meteorologists Joyfully Skip Under Noxious Pachyderms (or, sometimes, Purulent Narwhals). There. Easy, wasn't it? And don't forget Planet X, of course; not that you would.

There's no particular point about learning the planetary positions: it just makes you look clever. Accept another glass of your host's Chianti while you launch into a fascinating account of the meteorology of. . .

Mercury

Mercury hasn't got an atmosphere and consequently has *absolutely no Weather at all*. Isn't that exciting?! It's also useful if you find yourself stuck in a trainful of bores all droning on about the awful weather, the frozen points at Effingham Junction, and the monotonous changeability of the British Climate: "Where," you can ask, "would we be without it?"

Where we would be without it is, in fact, approximately 60 million miles from the nearest Wintry Shower;

temperatures in all areas would be in the region of 500°C
(1060°F) falling to −200°C (−424°F) at night, which lasts
about 29 days (or nights). This would very possibly lead to
signal failure at Coulsdon South.

Mercury takes only 88 days to orbit the Sun, so its
seasons are very short – or would be, if it had any.
Mercury is a bit like Miami without the vice and the
oranges.

Venus

Venus is named after the Roman Goddess of Marital
Relationships, which goes a long way towards explaining
the Decline and Fall. Venus is a planetary version of Los
Angeles; its atmosphere is very dense, comprises a single
area of High Pressure (about 1,350lbs/sq″) and is absolutely unbreathable, being mostly composed of carbon
dioxide.

Bluffers with a further degree in Global Warming can
extract a lot of mileage from this: "Venus," you can say, "is
where the Earth will be if we don't stop exporting fridges
to the Trobriand Islands. Makes you think, doesn't it?"
Really, it's just as well humans haven't got eight armpits.

A typical weather forecast for Venus would be: hot and
muggy, with temperatures rising to 475°C in sheltered
inland areas and squally showers of sulphuric acid. This
will also be a typical weather forecast for Birmingham
unless we do something about deodorant junkies.

Venus rotates in the opposite direction to all the other
planets; it is thus composed entirely of Southern Hemisphere and suffers terribly from the Minogue.

Earth

See page 7 and start again, if you're a moron.

Mars

Mars has polar ice caps, which at one time led scientists to believe that some form of intelligent life (or at any rate some form of Sir Ranulf Twistleton-Wickham-ffienes) might be possible there. It also has what appeared at one time to be canals, which probably explains why Col Nasser claimed the planet for Egypt in 1956 and Ronald Reagan described it in 1985 as 'a vital area of American, uh, jellybeans.' Fortunately, neither theory is correct: scientific tests carried out in the seventies by *Viking I* and II have proved beyond a shadow of a doubt that there is not, nor has there ever been, life on Mars. Probably.

Mars has a very thin atmosphere and consequently very weedy Weather, not at all like our good, solid, British stuff. A rough Earth equivalent to the Martian Weather would be a typical September afternoon in Dead Man's Crotch, Illinois. At midday on the equator the temperature can rise to 10°C (50°F) which is below average for Britain (except for you-know-where). The landscape is scarred with ancient flash-flood river beds, probably as a result of Prolonged Periods of Heavy Rain, Wintry In Places a very long time ago. The outlook for the next few billion years is Cool, with dust storms in all areas – just like East Anglia.

What little is left of the Martian atmosphere is leaking away into space at an alarming rate and therefore *must be going somewhere*; the answer is obvious to any self-respecting bluffer: see **The Bermuda Triangle**.

Jupiter

Jupiter is huge and mainly gaseous; the solid part of the planet is really quite small. This means that most of what we see of Jupiter is, in fact, its atmosphere. This is Very Exciting because it means that at least 70 per cent (say) of Jupiter is *composed entirely of Weather*. The proof of this, incidentally, lies in the Newtonian formula:

$$\frac{P}{S} = \frac{a^3}{A^3} \frac{T^2}{t^2}$$

. . . which means, of course, that the weather will remain unsettled for some time to come.

Jupiter has a Great Red Spot (the Gorbachev Effect) 2½ times the size of Earth. This is now known to be a real Mother of a Deep Depression leading to perpetual hurricanes, a catastrophic rise in house insurance premiums and an indefinite suspension of the JoveRail timetable with Bank Holiday services in all regions, though temperatures at ground level (if indeed there is one) are around 80°F ('Phew! Wotta 225mph Scorcha!' – *Sun*).

On the other hand, it probably rains a lot – well, all the time really – and for this reason Jupiter's application to join the EMS will be vetoed by Britain in order to preserve the sovereignty of the Headingly Test. The Jovian weather system operates in six-year cycles, just like droughts in the South of England, and this makes forecasting quite easy: wet and windy, with wetter and windier weather to come; temperatures about average for the time of epoch.

Saturn

Forget the rings: no Weather there: vastly overrated. But Saturn itself is even more Weathery than Jupiter; it is 80 per cent Complex Frontal Systems (a bit like the Mid Atlantic) and perpetually cloudy (a bit like Halifax, Nova Scotia). It manages wind speeds of 1,100 mph (a bit like ten Shetlands laid end to end). Viewed through a large telescope Saturn displays a fascinating array of atmospheric cloud systems, especially if you haven't bothered to clean the lens. A British Foreign Office survey probe (*Mendacity II*) concluded it was a bloody awful place, incapable of supporting civilised life, and therefore an ideal destination for unwanted immigrants.

Saturn's biggest moon, Titan, has a smoggy atmosphere the colour of tomato soup and high in nitrogen. Beneath this is a sea of murky red chemical pollutant which deposits layers of tar and heavy hydrocarbons on the ocean bottom and island surfaces. Both ocean and atmosphere contain the basic proteinous elements essential to the eventual evolution of organic life. Tritan is, in other words, a sort of planetiod Mediterranean holiday resort.

Uranus

This planet is probably better pronounced 'YoorAYnus' (as in what you're bluffing through) rather than 'YOOR-inus' (as in the content of your bluff). For Meteoroastrolographers, Uranus is pretty well the most thrilling thing since Horlicks: previously only known as a small white out-of-focus blob, this Amazing Wonder Planet is know known, thanks to the multi-billion dollar Weather Probe *Voyeur II*, to be, in fact, an altogether larger white out-of-focus blob. This is, of course, Unutterably Exciting – see, for instance, Moore & Fish: *1001 Unutterably Exciting Things About Uranus (Give Or Take 999 Or So)*.

In the Uranian year of 84 Earth years most of the time is spent having Winter, during which temperatures in remote Uranian glens reach −216°C. Its axis is tilted over at right angles to that of all the other planets, giving it a West Pole and an East Pole. This is, in all probability, the result of a worthy but futile attempt to avoid the Minogue.

45

Neptune

Neptune's atmosphere is composed almost entirely of North Sea Gas which, perversely enough, does not seem to have caused any degree of Planetary Warming. It suffers most piteously from a permanent Minogue and has a gigantic storm system similar to Jupiter's Great Red Spot except that it is

(a) smaller, and
(b) not red.

For this reason (maybe, why not?) it is known to insiders as the Fairly Large Greyish Thing On Neptune, in order to avoid confusion. (See Moore & Fish: *Some Really Quite Remarkable Things On Neptune, Including A Fairly Large Greyish One.*)

The atmosphere of Neptune shows up as bright blue, except when it's been computer-enhanced to appear red, or green, or greyish if you're watching in black and white on the kitchen portable. This is because it is methane (those wretched cows again) and therefore absolutely Wonderfuel, unless you want to breathe. Neptune also has high white clouds (Ufonimbus) *which actually cast shadows on the planet's surface*. This is Unbearably Thrilling.

Pluto

Pluto is small, hard, dark and frozen solid. Probably the remains of an eighteenth century hailstone. Sometimes it orbits closer to the Sun than Neptune, but it still hasn't had a book written about it or been made into a mini-series, not even a very late-night one for ethnic lesbians on Channel Four.

Weather: probably.

Planet X

Discovered last Tuesday by *Bluffo XIII*, Planet X is an idyllic world where warm, springlike weather alternates with languidly hot summers and the tangy thrill of autumn, and it always snows at Christmas. The pubs are open all day; formica and videogame machines have been outlawed by the Planetary Parliament, which meets once a century to uprate Planetary Benefits in line with inflation (which doesn't exist) and is dominated by Gladstonian Liberals, though not in overwhelming numbers.

Topographically, it combines the Scottish Highlands with the chocolate boxy bits of the Home Counties; there is also, here and there, a hint of pre-Nixon Cambodia and the more exciting parts of Iceland. Its single warm, self-cleaning sea is bounded by white sandy beaches, and anyone caught sailboarding or doing work-outs is made to write out 'It Is No Part Of The Human Heritage To Make An Idiot Of Oneself' a hundred times before being exiled to Uranus. The weather forecast is nearly always right and the Loch Ness Monster believes in everybody. It is where good bluffers go before they die.

The Sun

The Sun is, well, truly enormous; much bigger than Jupiter, for instance, and much *much* bigger than Pluto. It is of importance to Meteorobluffers for two reasons, viz:

1. **Solar Flares**
   Although unfashionable (like Solar Cuban Heels and Solar Kaftans) solar flares are of importance to us because:
   (a) they cause interference on Weather Forecast broadcasts

(b) they cause the Aurora Borealis and outbreaks of Temperance in Aberdeen, and

(c) they cause an increase in the second important thing, which is . . .

2. **Solar Wind**

All the time, the Earth's atmosphere is being bombarded with Completely Harmless Radiation at a speed of about 240 miles per second (except at Sellafield of course). This is the Solar Wind. During periods of sunspot activity, when huge eructations of solar energy occur as solar flares, the wind speed increases to 1.2 million miles per second. It stands to reason (if it doesn't then it certainly ought to) that this will cause all sorts of unexpected meteorological effects, especially of the sort that can't be blamed on Global Warming or the Minogue.

Solar flares are most active every eleven years or so and the next lot is due some time in 1994. During this time you should more or less be able to make up your weather forecasts as you go along, just like the professionals.

Eventually, in 12 billion years or so, the Sun will turn into a Red Giant. This is because it will need to burn more and more fuel, less and less efficiently, just to keep on producing energy; this is called the Magnox Effect. When this happens, the oceans will boil and the earth will melt; all the Fundamentalists will say 'Ya boo, told you so' and temperatures will reach 2,600°F (except in the Northern Asteroids). Our descendants will then be offered a choice between death and evacuation to Uranus. They will probably ask for time to think about it.

Comets

Comets are gigantic gritty snowballs (the sort we were told never to throw in the playground), only bigger. They are always visible somewhere else, just before dawn, when it's cloudy. They can also be seen (As Never Before) on all-night television space probe specials, where they turn out to look just like the computer-enhanced close-up of a tree frog's ovaries on last week's programme. You can sometimes spot artists' impressions of them on TV weather charts, though they only influence the climate when they collide with the latest malfunctioning European weather satellite, which isn't nearly often enough.

Meteors

Meteors are the origin of the word 'meteorological': true or false? False, unfortunately, but who cares. It is now generally accepted (except by people who disagree) that a really quite fabulously enormous meteor collided with Earth some 65 million years ago and wiped out 90 per cent of all life forms, including the dinosaurs but not the Loch Ness Monster. This was because it sent up a huge plume of dust, bits of pterodactyl, etc., into the Smogosphere and blotted out all the sunlight for a few years, or centuries, or something. This is good news for bluffers because volcanoes have the same effect, though on a smaller scale, as of course do smaller meteors.

Your procedure when caught out in a failed Fine Weather Bluff is, therefore, as follows:

1. Blame it on a meteor impact somewhere;
2. Agree that there haven't been any reports of meteor impacts but point out that
3. This is almost certainly a cover-up organised by the BBC/ITN/CIA/KGB/MI6/London Weather Centre/ the Freemasons, etc. because
4. You happen to know they were all at Cambridge in the twenties and
5. We all know what that means, don't we?

6. It could be a volcano . . .
7. Or the San Andreas Fault – but certainly not yours.

Failing this, your last recourse is either to **Chaos** *(q.v.)* or . . .

The Bermuda Triangle

The Bermuda Triangle is supposed to be very mysterious for the following reasons:

- It isn't really a triangle;
- It isn't in Bermuda;
- Of 28 ships lost off the US coast in 1976, only 6 were lost there: this can't be a coincidence.

However, you know better. The Not-Bermuda Polygon is, in fact, the place where all that Martian atmosphere is leaking to, in accordance with the Law of Conservation of Matter, the Treaty of Rome and Fish's Theorem, which states that Old Weather never dies but is endlessly recycled, especially in Wigan.

The Bermuda Triangle is thus the seed-bed of all the world's Occluded Fronts and the origin of our Complex Weather Systems: this is called the Hemingway Effect, and will shortly be made into a film by Steven Speilberg.

A much better explanation (because it happens to have some shreds of truth to clothe its impudence) of the phenomenon of meteorological cock-up may be found in **Chaos**. But first:

Flying Saucers

UFOs, as Astrobluffers call them, are, in fact, Uranian weather satellites sent to snoop around the Troposphere and take blobby out-of-focus photographs of the Mid-Atlantic Depression, the London Weather Centre, Budleigh Salterton, etc. Sometimes they land to let their crews stretch their tripods and take a few healthful breaths of carbon monoxide. On no account should they be approached; they are merely trying to ascertain whether the temperature is a degree or two above normal for the time of aeon and, if so, whether it might be a good idea to start thinking about setting up an Immigration Office.

AND NOW ...

CHAOS

This is your trump card, your Ace-in-the-Hole. Play it as often as you like; it's self-perpetuating, like your overdraft.

Chaos is the one solid gold nugget in the whole horrible toxic heap of Scientific Law, and there's nothing Real Scientists can do about it. It confirms what we, the splendid majority, have always known: namely that the whole point of Scientific Laws is that they don't work properly in Real Life. That failure in O-level Physics turns out, as you always suspected it would, to have been a wise move on your part.

The essence of Chaos is that a tiny, tiny, *tiny* deviation from the norm, anywhere in the world, can have a profoundly catastrophic effect on the one-way system in Oxford, and the best-laid plans of Mighty Experts have nothing whatever to do with it.

For instance: you may be tempted to believe that the continuing stability of the pound sterling depends on the Chancellor's adherence to austere limitations on Broad Money as encapsulated in the Treasury policy vis-a-vis sterling M3 and M4. Forget it. What happens in real life is that a prawn packer in Bombay sneezes into the production line, thereby producing a duff vindaloo in a

City take-away and a corresponding Run on the Pound in the markets the next morning.

You get the hang of it?

It's called the Butterfly Effect, because the illustration scientists themselves use is that of *a tropical butterfly whose erratic wing-beats may affect Atlantic weather systems.*

What is splendid about all this is that the wretched scientists are trying to formulate a Law of Chaos. It almost makes you feel sorry for them, doesn't it? Well all right then, no it doesn't – but what chance have all the weather men got against a bluffer armed with Chaos?

None.

So rush out – now – and get in something spiritous, and drink it off in honour of that marvellous butterfly. What? Well, thanks, that's very kind of you, I don't mind if I do. Cheers! *Sliànte mhor!*

Bluffer's Tip: Hurricanes

The October 1987 Tropospheric Effect was presaged by a sharp fall in air pressure, a change in the wind from SW to NE, and a drop of approximately 13°F in air temperature about twelve hours before it happened. Should these conditions occur again, forecast a hurricane. You still win if you're wrong: simply look at the next day's weather chart, draw your breath in sharply and say: "Phew! My God, that was close! Poor old Portugal."

THE WEATHER FORECASTER'S ALMANAC

A Month-by-Month Guide to the Meteorobluffer's Year

January

An unseasonal spell of fine weather (St Leofric's Little August Bank Holiday) causes sheep and cattle to lie down under upas trees in bewilderment. It is followed by 24 hours of snow which has been forecast well in advance and which catches no-one by surprise; British Rail have already cancelled all services as a precaution. Prices rise on the London Seaweed Exchange after heavy bidding by the National Union of Mineworkers.

February

Named after Fjbb, the Norse goddess of Sleet and mother of Snotta The Unprepared, February is traditionally the month of Staff Shortages, especially in Scotland where the Deep Depression that set in just after Hogmanay is only just beginning to break up. As usual (but nonetheless totally unexpectedly) heavy snow brings traffic grinding to a halt on Britain's roads (for explanation see **November**) and railways (see the blackboard at your local station). It is followed by unusually high temperatures, which are blamed on Global Warming, and flooding in Wales, which is blamed on the Tories.

March

The Vernal Equinox: clocks go forward, leading to rather less Weather at night than there was before. Temperatures now become 'Springlike' without actually going up at all, while showers continue to be Wintry in all areas except the Channel Islands and the Isle of Man, where they are free of tax. Proverbially, this month comes in like a lion (on Valium) and goes out like a lamb (on Steroids). Male hares rush around in a simulation of sexual frenzy which is in fact a rather pathetic attempt to keep warm.

April
A month of showers, one of which lasts a fortnight. A sudden Cold Snap (St Brünhilde's Little Habit) worries Britain's farmers, who put up the price of everything in anticipation of a poor harvest. An April Fool forecast on television goes completely unremarked, except by correspondents to the *Daily Telegraph*, who write in to comment on its remarkable accuracy, not that this in any way alters their views of course. Sheep and cattle lie down in despair. Traditionally the time of year when weather forecasters start predicting the weekend temperature values for Morocco.

May
Predictably quite a good month, with temperatures well above the normal for February, except in the Northern Isles. Network SouthEast crippled by sudden heat-expansion of track at Purley. Commencement of seasonally adjusted roadworks on the M6. Now is the time to begin looking wistfully at what's happening in Denmark, but don't hold your breath. Forecast rain on all the pseudo-folksy well-dressing maypole-type ceremonies the English Tourist Board would have us believe are traditional at this time of year.

June
This month contains the Summer Solstice, the only pagan ceremony the Christian Church never quite managed to find a space for; anthropologists now believe the Midsummer bonfires were originally an attempt to frighten away Deep Depressions in time for Wimbledon.

You can forecast lots of fine dry warm weather lasting right up to the opening match on Centre Court; thereafter, torrential rain especially around Dawn, who's still in the queue for tickets. The close season for Falkland Island invasions, June is also the month for forecasting freak hailstorms which just fail to help England avoid the follow-on. Remind people how much better the weather used to be, from the night-watchman's point of view, before They dropped Boycott. Very little Weather at night.

July

Usually warm, frequently very wet, July can nonetheless be relied upon to herald the commencement of hosepipe bans in the South-West and outbreaks of Hampstead in Tuscany. Humidity levels rise, but not enough to enable England bowlers to get the ball to turn. Pro-EMS left-wing bias detected in BBC weather forecasters who predict sizzling temperatures on the Continent; sharp increase in sales of WD40 as people in the Northern Isles attempt to unzip their parkas. Summer declared officially Open as Michael Fish takes his tie off.

August

The beginning of Autumn, and the month designated for the taking of British Summer Holidays. 'St Wulfstan's Little November' spoils the Bank Holiday Weekend. Weather becomes changeable between Disappointing and Bloody Sickening, When You Consider We'll Be Back At Work Next Week. The first Wintry Shower begins its long pilgrimage from the Bermuda Triangle; migrating birds queue up at NHS clinics for inoculations.

September

Winter Sales begin. The weather becomes manically changeable, with a fine, dry, hot spell about the beginning of the School Year ('St Trinian's Little Joke'). Forecast snow in Moscow by way of compensation, and stop looking wistfully at Denmark; a High Pressure Area there now means fog and another five miles added to the fifteen mile tailback on the M6 that's been there since June. Sheep and cattle stand up out of ennui.

October
The Autumn Equinox; clocks go back and overnight rain is forecast in all areas, particularly those where it's rained all day as well. The first snow in Aviemore paralyses commuter services into Charing Cross. Michael Fish predicts a hurricane, just to be on the safe side. Flooding in Wales blamed on holiday cottages. Hosepipe ban in South-West extended as reservoirs overflow into nearby toxic waste holding tanks.

November
A sudden wholly unforseeable outbreak of dry, fine, clear weather (St Ecfrith's Little Whitsun) brings warnings of frost and icy roads; councils use up their entire winter supply of rock salt and gravel as Heavy Drizzle halts traffic on the M6. Annual ceremony of Wet Leaves at Norbury. Letter to *The Times* reports sighting of a Sunny Period in Lerwick.

December
Annual festival of Stratocumulus held on the 25th. Winter Solstice; forecast long periods of uninterrupted moonshine. Millions watch as Michael Fish unwraps his Christmas cardigan and forecasts outbreaks of goodwill in all areas except the Lebanon. British Rail closes down altogether in a pre-emptive bid to avoid disruption in January. 'St Vortigern's Little Apocalypse' brings showers of giant Venusian frogs.

Old Bluffer's Maxim

> *If the Weather did not exist, it would be necessary
> to invent it.*
>
> Voltaire (1694-1778)

Only you, along with a handful of weather men, know this
is only half true.

The one lesson you ought to have hauled in by now is
this:

YOU NEED NEVER BE WRONG.

Follow this Guide, observe the Golden Rule, drink your
malt (Talisker, if you're buying), and you never will be.

Off you go, and the very best of luck.

Mind, we should take a mac if we were you.

GLOSSARY

Meteorology – the science (no, really, don't laugh) of weather forecasting; a sort of cross between Sociology, Aromatherapy and the I Ching; now a recognised religion in the US.

Meteorologist – one who practices Meteorology in the vain hope of one day becoming good at it.

Weather forecaster – sort of Meteorologist. Inclined to talk very fast on account of not being taken terribly seriously by the Head of Programmes.

outlook – changeable

further outlook – unsettled

long-term outlook – seasonal

sunny interval – short period of sunshine between two periods of rain.

sunny period – long interval of sunshine between two showers.

prolonged sunny period – sunshine that keeps weekday office hours.

unbroken sunshine with light overnight rain – summer forecast on Planet X.

shower – short period of rain between two longer ones.

scattered shower – as above, but in instalments.

wintry shower – outbreak of snow, sleet, hail, cold rain, etc., from October to April inclusive.

freak shower – outbreak of above during May, June, July, August.

gusting – a little trick a gale has of knocking you flat just as you've got used to walking at an angle of 45°.

cold front – on a weather map, a line of colder weather bringing showers and sunny intervals to the areas over which it passes.

warm front – on a weather map, a line of warmer weather bringing rain, scattered showers, and fleeting sunny moments.

occluded front – on a weather map, a line with bumps and triangles bringing unsettled, changeable weather with risks of flood, frost, drought, blizzards, etc. in all areas except the Channel Islands, where only disgustingly rich people are allowed to live (the Bergerac Effect).

weather front – (a) the next lot of Deeply Depressing Tropospheric Effects moving in from the Atlantic; (b) paramilitary guerilla organisation with links to Libya's Colonel Ghaddafi who plan to overthrow the Meteorological Establishment, and reinstate Sir Peter 'Parka' as head of Unavoidable Delays on British Rail.

weather station – sophisticated pseudo-scientific installation dedicated to forecasting what the weather was like yesterday.

all-weather satellite – hugely expensive malfunctioning Euro-Probe enabling us to find out where the clouds were five hours ago.

spy satellite – expensive means of finding out how much snow is falling in Siberia and broadcasting the information on the BBC World Service, thus undermining the Soviet public's confidence in the weather forecasts on the back page of *Pravda*.

wrong – anyone who suggests the above might be rather a waste of money these days.

radar – meteorological device for finding out whether it's raining or not.

radar picture – map of UK rainfall produced by English radar and consequently showing Scotland to be in the grip of an everlasting Dry Spell.

Republic of Ireland – large area to the south of Ulster which never has any Weather at all.

phew! – newspaper headline when the temperature exceeds 75°F in August.

brrr! – newspaper headline when it falls below freezing in January.

nippy/parky/raw/taters/brass monkeys – colloquial terms for unexpected cold weather in winter.

brisk/fresh/breezy/better today, eh? – colloquial terms for gale force winds in the Northern Isles.

National forecast – 90-second prediction of the weather for the whole country plus a look at the weekend prospects for Eastern Europe (changeable, with complex Ideological Fronts breaking up all over the place).

Regional forecast – Detailed 45-second look at the weather for your area, which is always different, especially if you've switched channels.

Shipping forecast – highly reliable means of forecasting the weather for anyone at sea, and consequently a closely guarded secret (except in Bailey, Fair Isle, Faroes, etc.).

complex – any Tropospheric Effect not really understood and/or completely unpredictable.

the weather – complex.

weather records – amaze your friends with the following:

Highest temperature (in the shade): 136°F, San Louis, Mexico, 1933.

Ditto in the UK: 98°F in Northants, Surrey and Kent, August 1911. Point out this was during a Liberal government.

Lowest temperature −128°F in Vostok, Antarctica, 1983.

Lowest UK temperature −17°F, Braemar, Scotland, 1982. Widely blamed on the Tories.

The largest recorded hailstone weighed 1.67lbs and fell on your grandfather in Kansas in 1970.

The most rain during a 24-hr period was 73.62 inches falling at Cilaos, Ile de Réunion, in 1952. The MCC touring team still lost by 8 wickets. The UK record is 11 inches at Martinstown, near Dorchester in 1955 ('St Jude's Little Monsoon').

Minimum UK sunshine: Westminster; there was no sunshine at all during December 1890. Point out (a) that this was during a Tory government; (b) that there is a place called Whitehall in Orkney.

Most wonderful summer ever: when you were little.

THE AUTHOR

David Milsted used to live in the Northern Isles, where he experienced a lot of Weather. He now lives in Skye with his wife, writer Jan Holt, and four children who don't believe a word of him. As a one-time Liberal candidate he knows a fair bit about Chaos and feels it ought to have a go at the balance of payments.

A rather occluded 36, he is the author of *The Chronicles of Craigfieth*, and its follow-up *Market Forces* which the *Times Literary Supplement* describes as 'a more genial, less dirty, Tom Sharpe view of Scottish country life' that 'could well become a cult, even south of the Border.'

THE BLUFFER'S GUIDES

Available at £1.95 each:

Accountancy	Literature
Advertising	Management
Antiques	Marketing
Archaeology	Maths
Ballet	Music
Bird Watching	Occult
Bluffing	Opera
Class	Paris
The Classics	Philosophy
Computers	Photography
Consultancy	Poetry
Cricket	Public Speaking
EEC	Publishing
Espionage	Racing
Feminism	Secretaries
Finance	Seduction
Fortune Telling	Sex
Golf	Teaching
Hi-Fi	Television
Hollywood	Theatre
Japan	University
Jazz	Wine
Journalism	Weather Forecasting

All these books are available at your local bookshop or newsagent, or can be ordered direct from the publisher. Just tick the titles you require and fill in the form below. Prices and availability subject to change without notice.

Ravette Books Limited, 3 Glenside Estate, Star Road, Partridge Green, Horsham, West Sussex RH13 8RA.

Please send a cheque or postal order, and allow the following for postage and packing: UK 25p for one book and 10p for each additional book ordered.

Name ....

Address..

....

....

THE BLUFFER'S GUIDES

Planned or in preparation:

Architecture
Beliefs
Contemporary Cinema
Defence
Foreign Affairs
Gambling
Greenism
Law
Modern Art
Motoring
Politics
Psychology
Public Relations
Rugby
Selling
Ski-ing

The USA
The Australians
The British
The French
The Germans